Written by Judy Wiltshire

Illustrated by Gemma Denham

ISBN 978-1-5272-7552-2

For my son Daniel, who loves the moon.

I Love
The Moon

I love the moon,
so shiny and bright.
But it always looks different
from night to night.

At times it looks like a big golden ball...

But sometimes, half of it's lost from sight.

And sometimes it's hardly there at all.

Sometimes it
disappears from sight,

leaving the stars to
light the night.

It's time for bed and I'm tucked in tight,

I wonder how it looks tonight.

I look up at the sky
for one last peep,
so I'll dream of the moon
when I fall asleep.

New Moon:

We cannot see
the Moon
when it is
a new moon

Waxing
Crescent:

A thin crescent
opening to
the right

First
Quarter:

The first
quarter phase
is seen as a
half moon

Waxing
Gibbous:

Between a
half moon and
full moon.
Waxing means
getting bigger

The Moon displays these eight phases one after the
other as it moves through its cycle each month.

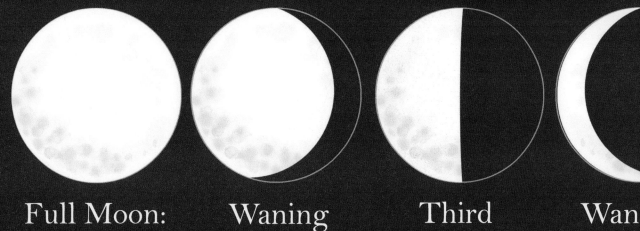

Full Moon:

The moon
is completely
illuminated

Waning
Gibbous:

Between a
half moon and
full moon.
Waning means
getting smaller

Third
Quarter:

The third quarter
moon is seen as a
half moon too,
but on the opposite
side to the
first quarter moon

Waning
Crescent:

A thin crescent
opening
to the left

It takes 27 days for the Moon to orbit Earth.
That means the Moon's cycle is 27 days long.

Printed in Great Britain
by Amazon

Printed in Great Britain
by Amazon